THE
Tin Whistle Tune Book
Thirty-Eight Tunes Appropriate for Tin Whistle, Fife, Flute, or Violin

Compiled and Arranged
by William E. White

Colonial Williamsburg
The Colonial Williamsburg Foundation
Williamsburg, Virginia

2025 24 23 22 21 20 19 18 17 16 15 14   20 21 22 23 24 25

ISBN 978-0-87935-051-2   79-26872

Printed in the United States of America

Colonial Williamsburg is a registered trade name of
The Colonial Williamsburg Foundation,
a not-for-profit educational institution.

The Colonial Williamsburg Foundation
PO Box 1776
Williamsburg, VA 23187-1776
www.colonialwilliamsburg.org

CONTENTS

PREFACE

THE TIN WHISTLE or penny whistle has experienced a rebirth in recent years that is linked in many ways to the rising interest in the traditional or folk customs, lore, and music that make up our heritage. This primitive instrument is still used extensively in Irish traditional music, and others are discovering how versatile an instrument it truly is.

It is difficult to determine exactly how or where the tin whistle originated. Historical references give us little help, since through the ages it has apparently been considered too simple and common an instrument to deserve much written comment. The whistle belongs to the family of "fipple flutes," which also includes the recorder of Renaissance origin. The true beauty of the instrument lies in its simplicity. Easily learned by almost anyone with a few minutes to devote to memorizing its fingering patterns, it can be played by a more experienced performer with such expression as to lift one's soul or move one to tears.

The music compiled here is only a sampling of what may be played. It has been drawn from several printed and manuscript sources of the eighteenth century. The Henry Beck and Edward Murphy manuscripts as well as

Benjamin Carr's two publications, *Evening Amusement* and *The Gentleman's Amusement*, are typical of the popular music available to Americans in the last quarter of the eighteenth century. It should be noted, however, that this music is not distinctively American. For the most part, music in the eighteenth century was an imported commodity that came to the New World in the form of publications from Europe (mainly the British Isles) or by immigrants who brought their music and instruments with them. Other sources are typical of the popular music of the period, much of which can still be heard today. Tunes such as "Soldiers Joy" and "Fishers Hornpipe" have their origins in eighteenth-century popular music and are still part of the basic repertoire for the modern folk musician.

No attempt has been made to alter or "improve" upon the melodies; they are presented just as they appear in the original sources. This, however, should not inhibit the performer by giving the impression that the music must be played exactly as written. The performance of the music is greatly enhanced by some improvisation. The addition of grace notes, slurs, and other ornaments is basic to the tin whistle style of playing, and as is customary with this type of music, I have chosen to leave such embellishments to the discretion of the performer.

Likewise, tempi are left to the performer's interpretation. The common time reels and marches, as well as the six-eight jigs, may be played as quickly or as slowly as the performer's ability and the tune itself will permit. The airs have been indicated by using the simple designation "slowly" beneath the first line and it is not necessary to keep a strict tempo. The music becomes much more expressive if the tempo within the piece is altered from time to time.

Although this book has been compiled for the tin whistle, the melodies contained herein may also be played on other instruments. Performers on fife, flute, or violin will discover that this music may easily be played on their instruments without altering key signatures.

I would like to extend my thanks to John C. Moon and Herbert E. Watson, my colleagues, for their help with and encouragement of my musical endeavors, and to the members of the Colonial Williamsburg Fifes and Drums who have performed much of this music for our visitors and have proven that it can be both challenging and enjoyable.

SOURCES OF THE MUSIC

Aird
A Selection of Scotch, English, Irish, and Foreign Airs Adapted to the Fife, Violin, or German-Flute. In six volumes. Glasgow, Printed and Sold by James Aird; and Glasgow, Printed and Sold by F. McFadyen [1782 – 1800]. Aird died before the completion of the sixth volume, which was printed by McFadyen along with reprints of the other volumes. This very popular work saw as many as seven editions by various printers.

Beck Manuscript
A bound manuscript volume in the Music Division of the Library of Congress. The flyleaf proclaims it to have been "Mary Mathers Book. 1810," while an interior page bears the inscription, "Copied by Henry Beck in the Year 1786."

Carr, *Evening Amusement*
Evening Amusement Containing Fifty Air's, Song's Duett's, Dances, Hornpipe's, Reel's, Marches, Minuett &c, &, for 1, and 2 German Flutes or Violins. Printed & sold at B. Carr's Musical Repositories Philadelphia and New York & J. Carr's Baltimore [1796].

Carr, *Gentlemans Amusement*
The Gentlemans Amusement A Selection Of Solos, Duetts, Overtures, arranged as Duetts, Rondos & Romances . . . Printed for the Editors and Sold at B. Carr's Musical Repositories Philadelphia and New York and J. Carr's Baltimore [ca. 1794 – 1796].

Fentum
The Compleat Tutor For the German Flute Containing the Best and Easiest Instructions for Learners to Obtain a Proficiency. Translated from the French To which is added a Choice Collection of ye most Celebrated Italian, English & Scotch Tunes; Curiously Adapted to that Instrument. Printed for and Sold by Jonathan Fentum at his Musick Shop in Exeter Exchange in the Strand, London [ca. 1765].

Murphy Manuscript
A bound manuscript book in the collection of the Library of Congress bearing the inscription "Newport [Rhode Island?] Edward Murphy October 26 - 1790."

Orpheus Caledonius
Orpheus Caledonius: Or, A Collection of Scots Songs. Set to

Musick By W. Thomson. The Second Edition. Two volumes. London: Printed for the Author, at his House in Leicester-Fields. 1733.

Oswald
The Caledonian Pocket Companion Containing Fifty of the *most favourite Scotch Tunes several of them with Variations, all set for the German Flute, by Mr. Oswald.* In six volumes. London Printed for T. Simpson in Sweeting's Alley opposite the East Door of the Royal Exchange [ca. 1745]. This popular work went through several editions and was eventually expanded to include fifteen volumes.

INSTRUCTIONS FOR PLAYING
THE TIN WHISTLE

THE TIN WHISTLE is an extremely easy instrument to learn. Producing a sound is done simply by blowing lightly through the mouthpiece. By nature the tin whistle is a soft instrument, and undertones or over-pitching will occur if you blow too hard.

Once you have produced a sound tone, cover the finger holes with the first three fingers of each hand, using the left hand to cover the top three holes and the right hand the bottom three. Then look at the fingering chart on the next page. Lift your fingers as indicated to play each note.

Tin whistles are made in various keys. For example, a whistle in the key of "C" produces the note "C" when all the finger holes are covered. Likewise, a whistle in the key of "D" produces the note "D" when all of the finger holes are covered. The player, however, always thinks of the lowest note on the whistle as "D" regardless of its actual pitch.

The tin whistle is extremely limited in the keys in which it plays, being almost totally restricted to G Major, D Major, and their relative minors. Accidental notes can be produced but usually occur when you cover only half a hole, which causes, at best, variations in pitch. I have tried to avoid these accidentals in the music (with the exception of an occasional G sharp), but have provided a separate fingering chart for accidental notes.

The beginning performer may find that it is much easier to sound each note of the music individually, or to tongue behind the teeth. This is acceptable initially. Eventually, however, you should attempt to play without sounding each individual note. A more flowing technique can be achieved by slurring passages together, phrasing groups of notes, and differentiating and emphasizing notes by using grace notes and ornaments.

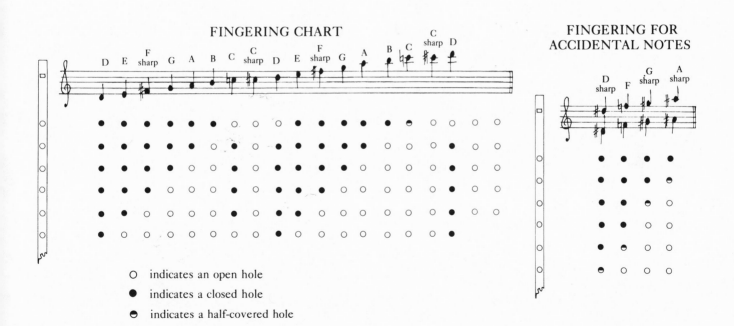

FINGERING CHART

FINGERING FOR ACCIDENTAL NOTES

O indicates an open hole

● indicates a closed hole

◐ indicates a half-covered hole

THE WHITE COCKADE

Carr, *Evening Amusement*

THE HIGH ROAD TO LINTON

Aird, Vol. 4

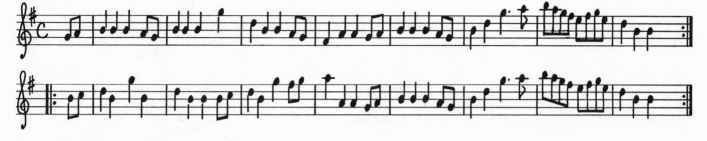

THE YORK FANCY

Aird, Vol. 3

THE BARRING OF THE DOOR

Aird, Vol. 2

THE PEACOCK

Aird, Vol. 2

CARLEN IS YOUR DAUGHTER READY

Aird, Vol. 1

SOLDIERS JOY

Carr, *Evening Amusement*

TRIP TO THE LITTLE THEATRE

Beck Manuscript

CLIFTON SPRINGS

Beck Manuscript

13

THE SUN FROM THE EAST

Beck Manuscript

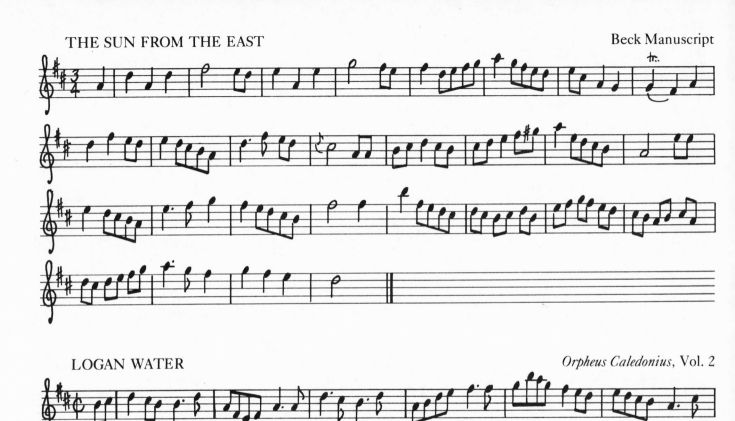

LOGAN WATER

Orpheus Caledonius, Vol. 2

Slowly

14

THE LADS OF THE VILLAGE

Aird, Vol. 1

THE ROSE TREE

Carr, *Evening Amusement*

JACK ON THE GREEN

Beck Manuscript

SIR JOHN MALCOLM

Aird, Vol. 2

MY NANNY-O

Orpheus Caledonius, Vol. 1

Slowly

LADY HARRIOT HOPE'S REEL

Aird, Vol. 2

QUICK STEP THE TROOPERS

Aird, Vol. 1

BLACK MARYS HORNPIPE

Murphy Manuscript

SHILLEY O GUIRE

Beck Manuscript

17

THE BOTTOM OF THE PUNCH BOWL

Oswald, Vol. 1

THE BONNIEST LASS IN A' THE WORLD

Oswald, Vol. 2

WHEN BIDDEN TO THE WAKE OR FAIR

Carr, *Evening Amusement*

Slowly

FISHERS HORNPIPE

Carr, *Evening Amusement*

19

LASS GIN YE LOE ME TELL ME NOW

Aird, Vol. 2

THE COUNTRY BUMKINS

Beck Manuscript

ANDREW CAREY

Aird, Vol. 5

THE LASS OF PEATY'S MILL

Orpheus Caledonius, Vol. 1

Slowly

THE ABERDEENS SCOTS MEASURE

Oswald, Vol. 5

THE EMPTY PURSE

Aird, Vol. 5

THE JOLLY GAYPEDLAR

Carr, *Gentleman's Amusement*

GI'E THE MAWKING MAIR O'T

Oswald, Vol. 3

WELL A GO TO KELSO

Aird, Vol. 2

WILL YOU GO TO SHERIFF MUIR

Oswald, Vol. 6

AN THE KIRK WAD LET ME BE

Beck Manuscript

THROW THE WOOD LADDIE

Orpheus Caledonius, Vol. 1

Slowly

THE BANKS OF SPEY

Aird, Vol. 5

OVER THE WATER TO CHARLIE WITH THE VARIATIONS

Fentum

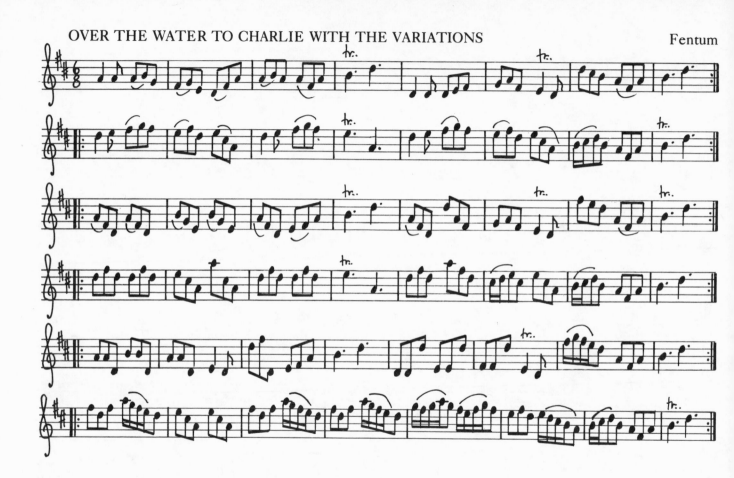